The Lady of Shalott

by Alfred, Lord Tennyson

edited by Christine Hall and Martin Coles

Setting the scene

Tennyson's poem about the Lady of Shalott is set in medieval times. Tennyson includes the famous knight, Sir Lancelot, in his poem. Sir Lancelot was one of the Knights of the Round Table who served King Arthur. He was a handsome, brave, romantic and daring figure. In this poem, however, he does not realise the sacrifice that the Lady of Shalott has to make just to look at him directly.

The Lady of Shalott has been a very popular poem ever since it was written over 150 years ago. It has also inspired many paintings and drawings.

Part 1

On either side the river lie
Long fields of barley and of rye,
That clothe the wold and meet the sky;
And through the field the road runs by
　　To many-tower'd Camelot;
And up and down the people go,
Gazing where the lilies blow
Round an island there below,
　　The island of Shalott.

wold hills

Willows whiten, aspens quiver,
Little breezes dusk and shiver
Through the wave that runs for ever
By the island in the river
  Flowing down to Camelot.
Four grey walls, and four grey towers,
Overlook a space of flowers,
And the silent isle imbowers
  The Lady of Shalott.

aspen *type of tree*
imbowers *closes around*

3

By the margin, willow veil'd,
Slide the heavy barges trail'd
By slow horses; and unhail'd
The shallop flitteth silken-sail'd
    Skimming down to Camelot:
But who hath seen her wave her hand?
Or at the casement seen her stand?
Or is she known in all the land,
    The Lady of Shalott?

shallop boat
casement window

Only reapers, reaping early,
In among the bearded barley
Hear a song that echoes cheerly
From the river winding clearly;
    Down to tower'd Camelot;
And by the moon the reaper weary,
Piling sheaves in uplands airy,
Listening, whispers, "'Tis the fairy
    The Lady of Shalott."

sheaves
bundles of corn

5

art II

There she weaves by night and day
A magic web with colours gay.
She has heard a whisper say,
A curse is on her if she stay
　　To look down to Camelot.
She knows not what the curse may be,
And so she weaveth steadily,
And little other care hath she,
　　The Lady of Shalott.

And moving through a mirror clear
That hangs before her all the year,
Shadows of the world appear.
There she sees the highway near
　　Winding down to Camelot;
There the river eddy whirls,
And there the surly village churls,
And the red cloaks of market girls
　　Pass onward from Shalott.

web a tapestry or woven cloth
churls rough village men

Sometimes a troop of damsels glad,
An abbot on an ambling pad,
Sometimes a curly shepherd lad,
Or long-hair'd page in crimson clad
    Goes by to tower'd Camelot;
And sometimes through the mirror blue
The knights come riding two and two.
She hath no loyal Knight and true,
    The Lady of Shalott.

damsels *girls*
abbot *head monk*
pad *horse*
page *knight's servant*

But in her web she still delights
To weave the mirror's magic sights,
For often through the silent nights
A funeral, with plumes and lights
    And music, went to Camelot;
Or when the moon was overhead,
Came two young lovers lately wed.
"I am half sick of shadows," said
    The Lady of Shalott.

Part III

A bow-shot from her bower-eaves,
He rode between the barley sheaves,
The sun came dazzling thro' the leaves,
And flamed upon the brazen greaves
   Of bold Sir Lancelot.
A red-cross Knight for ever kneel'd
To a lady in his shield,
That sparkled on the yellow field,
   Beside remote Shalott.

The gemmy bridle glitter'd free,
Like to some branch of stars we see
Hung in the golden Galaxy.
The bridle bells rang merrily
   As he rode down to Camelot:
And from his blazon'd baldric slung
A mighty silver bugle hung,
And as he rode his armour rung
   Beside remote Shalott.

bow-shot the distance an arrow can be shot from a bow
bower-eaves the edge of the roof by her room
brazen greaves brass leg armour
blazon'd baldric decorated belt

All in the blue unclouded weather

Thick-jewell'd shone the saddle-leather,

The helmet and the helmet-feather

Burn'd like one burning flame together,

    As he rode down to Camelot.

As often thro' the purple night,

Below the starry clusters bright,

Some bearded meteor, burning bright,

    Moves over still Shalott.

His broad clear brow in sunlight glow'd;
On burnish'd hooves his war-horse trode;
From underneath his helmet flow'd
His coal-black curls as on he rode,
    As he rode down to Camelot.
From the bank and from the river
He flashed into the crystal mirror,
"Tirra lirra," by the river
    Sang Sir Lancelot.

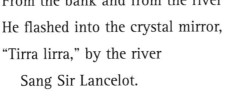

burnish'd shiny

13

She left the web, she left the loom,
She made three paces through the room,
She saw the water-lily bloom,
She saw the helmet and the plume,
   She look'd down to Camelot.
Out flew the web and floated wide;
The mirror crack'd from side to side;
"The curse is come upon me," cried
   The Lady of Shalott.

Part IV

In the stormy east-wind straining,
The pale yellow woods were waning,
The broad stream in his banks complaining.
Heavily the low sky raining
   Over tower'd Camelot;
Down she came and found a boat
Beneath a willow left afloat,
And around about the prow she wrote
   The Lady of Shalott.

waning growing weaker

And down the river's dim expanse
Like some bold seer in a trance,
Seeing all his own mischance –
With a glassy countenance
   Did she look to Camelot.
And at the closing of the day
She loosed the chain, and down she lay;
The broad stream bore her far away,
   The Lady of Shalott.

seer someone who can see into the future

mischance bad luck

countenance face

Lying, robed in snowy white
That loosely flew to left and right –
The leaves upon her falling light –
Thro' the noises of the night,
     She floated down to Camelot:
And as the boat-head wound along
The willowy hills and fields among,
They heard her singing her last song,
     The Lady of Shalott.

robed dressed

Heard a carol, mournful, holy,
Chanted loudly, chanted lowly,
Till her blood was frozen slowly,
And her eyes were darkened wholly,
  Turn'd to tower'd Camelot.
For ere she reach'd upon the tide
The first house by the water-side,
Singing in her song she died,
  The Lady of Shalott.

ere *before*

Under tower and balcony,
By garden-wall and gallery,
A gleaming shape she floated by,
Dead-pale between the houses high,
    Silent into Camelot.
Out upon the wharfs they came,
Knight and burgher, lord and dame,
And around the prow they read her name,
The Lady of Shalott.

burgher citizen

Lady of Sha

20

Who is this? And what is here?
And in the lighted palace near
Died the sound of royal cheer;
And they crossed themselves for fear,
   All the knights at Camelot:
But Lancelot mused a little space;
He said, "She has a lovely face;
God in his mercy lend her grace,
   The Lady of Shalott."

21

crossed themselves *made a sign of the cross*

mused *thought*

The language

- **Patterns** – each stanza is divided into two parts and the names 'Camelot', 'Shalott' or 'Lancelot' are repeated to make a pattern.

- **Rhymes** also help create a pattern. Within each stanza, lines 1–4 and lines 6–8 rhyme.

- **Direct speech** is used to create drama and tension in the poem (for example on pages 9 and 21).

of the poem

- **Colours** show how bright and handsome Sir Lancelot looks (for example on pages 10 and 12).

- **Simple language**, particularly verbs which emphasise action is used to add drama to the moment when the curse is broken (page 14).

- **Sad sounds and slow pace** create the atmosphere for the death of the Lady of Shalott (page 19).

Alfred, Lord Tennyson

Alfred Tennyson was born in Lincolnshire in England in 1809. He was one of twelve children. He was educated at home by his father. He started writing poetry while he was young, and at the age of twelve he wrote a 6,000-line poem. In 1827 he published a book of poems with his brother Charles. He continued to write and publish poems throughout his life.

From 1827 to 1831 Tennyson went to Cambridge University where he met his best friend, Arthur Hallam. When Arthur Hallam died in 1833, Tennyson wrote about his grief in a poem called *In Memoriam*, which was finally published in 1850. The poem became very famous, particularly because it was one of Queen Victoria's favourite poems. In 1850, Queen Victoria made Tennyson Poet Laureate.

Tennyson married Emily Sellwood in 1850. Their first child was born dead in 1851. Their second child survived and was called Hallam Tennyson. Tennyson's poems were very popular with the public – in 1859 he sold 10,000 copies of a new poem in one month. In 1883 Tennyson was made a Baron and became known as Lord Tennyson. Tennyson died in 1892.